A Prickle of Poems

by Judy Oliphant

*A collection of poems about nature,
life and other important things!*

50% of proceeds from the sale of this book will be donated to

Prickles in a Pickle
Reg. Charity No. 1189005

Printed and published in the UK in 2023
by South West Books UK

ISBN 978-1-9996930-8-4

Dedication

*Especially for my mum, Ann Freear,
my family and my partner
in life and rescue, Alan,
with love*

Contents

Spring

'Spring is here', the Snowdrop said,
'I wonder where it's been.
While I've been hiding underground.
Beneath the snow, unseen.'
'Are you sure?' the Robin asked,
'It still feels cold to me.'

Primrose shivered in her leaves,
'Too cold for me,' said she.
Catkin quivered on the branch,
High in the Hazel tree,
'The sun is out, but is still weak,
Still too weak for me!'

'Oh! Do come on,' Snowdrop said,
'Spring has sprung, you'll see'
Dandelion shook his golden head,
'I am afraid, I disagree,
There needs to be more sun about,
And some thirsty Bees.'

Celandine and Buttercup,
With their yellow gleam.
Already pushing through the earth
Up through a sea of green.
The sun looked down upon them all,
Her rays still watery.
'It won't be long, I'm getting strong.'

'Hang on and wait for me"
The Bluebells in their winter beds,
Were sleeping very deep.
Stitchwort too, was lying low,
As warm they tried to keep.

But once the Blackthorn starts to bloom,
Flowers before its leaves,
The rest of them will follow suit,
And wake up from their sleep.

Primrose

Petals soft as clotted cream,

In a cup of softest green.

Perfume rising in the sun

Telling us that spring has come.

Snowdrop

I am a little Snowdrop,
I love the ice and snow,

I show myself quite early,
so that you will know.

Spring is round the corner,
waiting in the wings.

Bringing you more flowers
and hope for better things.

'Dandy Lion' (Dandelion)

I am very underwhelming, a common little weed,
But if you look more closely, I have everything you need.
My leaves are green and tender, in salad they are fine,
My petals, soft and gentle, fermented, make great wine.

My roots can make you coffee, I'm a store of all things good,
Vitamins I have in plenty, I'm no ordinary food.
Antioxidants I have inside me, they purify the blood,
I fight your high cholesterol, I'm no ordinary bud.

In the past I was respected, revered and called a herb,
These days I'm pulled from gardens, relegated to the verge.
To bees and pollinators, I am the first thing that they see,
When they emerge from winter sleeping, cold and so hungry.

I raise my golden head up, and drink in all the sun,
Heralding to all who see me, spring has just begun.
The starving bees and insects, locate my sunny face,
They see a full oasis, in an otherwise empty space.

Please don't think me common, please don't pull me up,
I am the first spring flower for the bees to take their sup.
So, leave me if you find me, I will do no harm,
The bees will thank you later, as my petals keep them warm.

'The Hedge Row'

Once respected for the boundaries, we protected land within.
Arms of blackthorn, bramble, rosehip, hawthorn, maple, and catkin.
Honeysuckle with its fragrance, overpowering in the sun.
Rambles carelessly with the clematis and dog rose all as one.

At our feet a bed of chaos in the beauty of the grass.
Stitchwort, bluebell, parsley, and the primrose all amass.
These and many others grow in the shelter of our lap.
From spring right through the seasons until our winter nap.

The colours start as fresh and bright as early morning dew.
Until the dark of winter gives us a starker hue.
Those of us who are quite ancient are a different kind of hedge.
We take up much more ground space and crop yield it's alleged.

And so, to many landowners, we are no use to them today.
They create their needed borders in a different kind of way.
And to new developments of houses in the towns.
The diggers and the 'dozers are brought in to take us down.

But we have much more importance than being
guardians of your land.
There are many little creatures who live in where we now stand.
From little, tiny beings in the soil that you can't see.
To the butterflies and insects, birds and honeybees.

We are a home to many who are more important than you know.
We provide safe passage for all wildlife as they go.
Between the islands of the wilderness, the meadows, and the trees.
We are the highways for all creatures
needing places just like these.

The value of our presence is much higher than understood.
We need you to protect us and revere us as you should.
We carry much of history within our prickly arms.
Please keep us so we can continue to keep wildlife from harm.

Bluebell Wood

Dedicated to Dad and Chrissie

There is nothing like a bluebell wood,
To lift your spirits high.
Bell shaped flowers nod their heads'
As beech trees softly sigh.

Beneath the dappled canopy,
Whispered hush fills the air.
The sweetest scent intoxicates,
Silent creatures, sleeping there.

Standing in the dappled shade
Clouds of pollen gently rise.
Bees now stir from slumber deep,
Start to steal their golden prize.

There is nothing like a bluebell wood,
To soothe a troubled mind,
Take a stroll and soothe your soul,
And leave your cares behind.

Summer

Buckets and spades, suncream and 'shades',
Sand between toes, summery glows,

Splashes and shrieks, come from the beach,
As little pink toes, find water so cold.

Cornflower skies, birds flying high,
The buzzing of bees, the shade of the trees.

Barbeques smoking, hungry mouths hoping,
For hot tasty morsels, cooking on hot coals.

So summer is here, let's give it a cheer,
Drink in the sunshine, rejoice in the good times.

Buzz

I wear a fluffy jacket, of black and yellow hue,
Flying 'round the flowers with such a lot to do.
I pollinate the flowers as I go about my work.
I gather up the nectar, I have no time to shirk.

Back home I go to empty and store my precious load.
And once again go out once more to gather up the gold.
Back and forth I travel, in wind and rain and sun.
And only when the moon comes out my day of work is done.

Because of me the plants you grow, are able to provide,
The food you eat, the flowers you love and much more besides.
When you see me, don't freak out and bat me with your hand.
I am the little flying teddy bear that helps to bloom your land.

Rescue Me!

Rescue's never easy, we do what we can do,
Our hearts and souls are open, to heal and comfort you.
No matter if you're broken, sick or very sad.
We will try to mend you, so you don't feel so bad.
We talk in gentle voices and tell you all is well.
We keep you warm and comfy, the pain we will expel.
The medicines we give you will chase the bad away,
We will keep you safe and sound while with us you must stay.
Then one day you will return, back home where you belong.
So you can live your prickly life, now well and very strong.
But rescue works in many ways, sometimes you rescue us!
Humans break and feel unwell, suffer silently from stress.
So thank you little urchins, for needing us to help,
As, like many humans, we needed you as well.

Unseen

Suddenly the people came. And stayed at home all day.
I wondered what this change would mean.
Would I want to stay? This garden here has been my home.
Safe and full of food. I have had my children here.
Provided for my brood.

Some gardens I have visited,
Have no green at all,
They have this funny plastic stuff.
No gaps within their walls.
I cannot find the nourishment,
Within these sterile rooms,
No water there to quench my thirst.
What am I to do?

At night I start to forage,
For juicy worms and bugs,
I find a huge selection,
In a veg bed freshly dug.
The other place of plenty,
Is the compost heap,
It's always nice and warm in there,
Lovely for a sleep.

I have no need to travel far, And cross a busy road,
Or dice with death while passing by,
A Badgers' deep abode. All I need is here for me,
Within this garden green, And while people are in bed asleep,
I can roam about unseen.

I hear their conversations, As I slumber through the day,
A little girl's clear voice rings out, She's got a lot to say!
She tells her mum and dad, About the beetles and the bees.
How they are most important, And then she mentions me!

'We have a hedgehog here you know?' She tells them happily,
'You never see her come and go, She's very shy you see,
But I would like to help her out, And keep her safe and
sound, If we treat her well enough, She may stick around.

Hedgehogs are too few to find, We must take great care.
To keep our garden fresh and green, Not concrete slabs and
bare. We must build a house for her, And feed her every day.
And if she stays with us you see,
Her friends might come this way'.

And so, it seems this change in life,
People staying in their homes,
Is not a death knell to my ears,
But, instead is giving hope.
The more they have the time to see,
The garden life they missed.
The more, it seems, they start to see,
That wildlife is a gift.
To have us in their garden patch,
However big or small.
And to have a living garden green,
Brings joy to one and all.

The Ocean

Life at the bottom of the ocean,
Is as full as the shores up above.
Many creatures and plants live within it,
Filling the sea that we love.

From the largest who just eat the plankton.
Smallest only microscopes can see.
All of us admire and enjoy it.
From our oldest to toddlers so wee.

The ocean provides us with bounty.
Treasures so rich and so rare.
We need to take care how we treat them.
There is only so much we can share.

Rich fishing grounds that were once known.
Now just deserts under the sea.
The sea grass and kelp once in meadows.
Need to rest and just left to be.

We are starting to learn some lessons.
We are to look and take stock.
And know now the sea grass meadows.
So much carbon they can lock.

To understand is so important.
And it may be our saving grace.
To culture and save our ocean gardens
And make the world a better place.

The Forest

In the still of the forest, in the whisper of the trees,
You can bathe in the silence, and the green of the leaves.
The gentle air will soothe you, and cleanse you of sad thoughts.
The rhythm of the branches, give the healing that you sought.

The roots are connected through the soil on which you step.
They speak to each other along the fragile web.
Sending to each other the sustenance they need,
From each and every flower, every tree every weed.

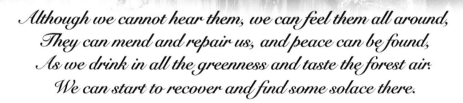

Although we cannot hear them, we can feel them all around,
They can mend and repair us, and peace can be found,
As we drink in all the greenness and taste the forest air.
We can start to recover and find some solace there.

Many creatures have their homes within the canopy of hush,
They hide amongst the branches, the trees and all the brush.
You may not get to see them as you wander in the wood.
Shy glimpses of a movement as they move from where they've stood.

The more we rush about and be so busy in our lives.
The more we need wild spaces to soothe us and to hide,
From all the hustle, and the noise and so many stressful things.
We need our wild green spaces and the peace that they all bring.

Nature

Nature looked down on the Earth, her heart was truly broken.
For what she saw beneath her feet, was utter desolation.
The guardians of her work, her world, the life she had created,
Betrayed her trust, destroyed her work, the beauty, they erased it.

She trembled as the rivers died, the seas and lakes polluted.
She shook her head and shed a tear to see the forests looted.
She gave the human life below, everything they needed.
But somehow, as the years went by, her love went by unheeded.

The people wanted more and more from the land they tended.
The crops they grew, were engineered, genetically blended.
A prairie landscape spread throughout; a desert was created.
Nitrates and chemicals sprayed in, so food demand was sated.

She saw the creatures of the earth, struggle for existence,
The fight they had to stay alive, tested their resilience.
The human beings, they took their homes, the habitat they lived in.
And one by one the creatures died, gave in to their extinction.

'Enough's, enough,' Nature roared, as she lost all patience.
'I will make you change your ways and earn back your allegiance',
Along came storms and fire and floods, an arsenal truly shocking.
The devastation was so vast, the earth was really rocking.

And then to really make her point, to make the people listen,
She made a virus visit them, an incurable infection.
Oh! How they wept and moaned and cried, as they died in thousands.
Hugs were banned, the schools were closed, they stayed
inside their homelands.

While governments discussed things, made rules,
and sought solutions,
It came to pass that while indoors there came a revolution.
People took a daily walk outside, to keep them fit and healthy,
They recognised more important things to that of being wealthy.

And now it seems we come full turn, right back to where we started,
Where Nature is our happy place, a friend from whom we parted.
We look towards the future now, the planet needs restoring,
Nature draws a breath, and settles down,
and prays that hope is dawning.

The Tree

I have stood here for one hundred years, and some so many more.
Watching clouds of change pass by, while standing true and sure.
When I was but a stripling, green stemmed and thinly limbed.
Surrounding me were many fields, and lots of living things.

I was the youngest generation, of others just like me.
All connected to each other, underground where you can't see.
All of us sent messages through a web of roots and spores.
We sent each other nutrients and water through the pores.

There were once so very many and now there are so few.
We stood together proudly providing shelter where we grew.
We drank the surplus water that would flood your precious homes.
The still and peace beneath our leaves, the best you've ever known.

Your children often climbed us and had picnics in the cool.
'The woods' they used to call us, running past from home to school.
The hedgerow ran around us, full of flora, birds and bees.
And then one day it was decided, you had a greater need.

No longer did the simple things, hold your interest long.
No longer did you find pleasure, in a blackbird's song.
Roads and bigger houses, not for families but for greed.
Aspiring to the adverts that tell you what you need.

And so now 'The Woods' have fallen, now all there is, is me.
An old oak tree with letters carved, that spell Bill loves Sally B.
I still supply the shelter I still provide a roost.
I have no friends to talk with, no nutrients to boost.

The fields around are covered now, with buildings, people, cars.
The landscape is now desolate, where once was life, are scars.
My roots tied in with tarmac, through which I cannot breathe.
I wonder now how long I have before I have to leave.

Occasionally an old man comes and stands beneath my boughs.
His fingers trace the letters carved into me below.
'Oh! Sally how I miss you', a tear runs down his cheek.
'But my dear, what have they done to where we used to meet?'

He looks at me with sad old eyes and pats me with his hand.
'Well old friend, thank you so, for continuing to stand'.
'A constant, in these times of change, a memory so dear'.
Of my life's love who now I have lost and used to kiss right here'.

He stays with me for a while, sharing thoughts that I could read.
Then he turns to leave and says, 'I wish people would take heed'.
'The only living thing we have, the one we do not need'.
'Is the human race, my friend, our world just must be freed'.

Autumn

Autumn is upon us, evenings getting cool.
The trees are changing colour to every kind of hue.
Fields are tilled and turned, as crops are stored away.
Grain stores filled and brimming, barns are full of hay.
Cupboards full of jam pots and pickles sweet and sour.
The darkness fills the sky, at a much earlier hour.
Food becomes more comforting, dumplings, stews and such.
Crumbles, pies and custard we love those far too much!
Freezers full of berries from the hedges we have picked.
Remind us of the sunshine, in the winter that we miss.

Harvest Festivals for the fruits of labour on the land.
Bounty shared amongst those who don't have much at hand.
For the creatures in the forests, the hedgerows and the trees.
It is a time for being busy, storing what they have all gleaned.
All nests and burrows cosy with gathered bits and bobs.
Every creature rushing round to finish all the jobs.
That need to be completed before winter comes along.
The birds that stay here with us sing a very different song.
All of us preparing for a winter very cold.
Looking to the spring again, as the sun becomes more bold.
Then everything awakes again and everything is new.
We all cheer up and smile and banish winter blues.

The
Hedgehog

I am a little Hedgehog,
I roam about at night.
If you see me in the daytime,
Something is not right.

If I am moving with some purpose,
With some leaves inside my nose,
Nest building in a hurry,
For my babies don't you know!

Unless my nest I'm building,
I do not venture out,
I do not like sunbathing,
I should not be wobbling about.

If you see me in your garden,
At any time of day.
Please call your local rescue.
And catch me, don't delay.

They will happily advise you,
And tell you what to do,
To help me and ensure that,
I'll come back to you.

Our numbers are so few now,
Please help us if you can.
Our lives are truly precious,
And are resting in your hands.

23

The River

High upon a hillside, I start my journey to the sea,
So small and insignificant, a tiny trickle me.
I push through all the undergrowth, peat and rocky soil,
And up into the sunshine, I bubble, and I boil.

I seep through all the marshes, creating habitat,
For wading birds and other things who like a nice mudflat.
On I travel getting wider, joining others just like me,
Over boulders we now tumble and race on happily.

As we grow, we fill with creatures who need us to survive,
And all around we leach out water, keeping other things alive.
On we rush through tended farmland, through villages and towns.
As we get wider and much deeper, we are much slower now.

Our chemistry it now alters, as we merge into the sea.
So now I am part of an enormous entity.
Although I am an ocean, and now I am so vast,
I will always carry with me where I came from in the past.

My beginning was so humble, so innocent and pure.
It will always be within me of that I am most sure.

Not Alone

Sometimes I just sit and think of how things used to be,
Without the cares and troubles that sometimes worry me.
A simple life wrapped within the family I love,
So many now, are angels, in heaven up above.

How nice to have a chat with my sister, aunt, and mum,
Ask them what they think about the woman I've become.
To talk about the world, how it's changed now they have gone,
I do not ask for lots of time, perhaps an hour, only one.

The family, it has grown again as families often do,
And sometimes there are issues that they could talk me through.
I try so hard to imagine what they would have to say,
I shared so much with all of them before they went away.

In the quiet of the night-time and the still before I sleep,
I can see them all quite clearly, my thoughts they softly keep.
They steal my woes and worries and take them all away,
So, I don't have to have them with me, and spoil another day.

Our loved ones never leave us, their spirit lingers on,
In our hearts we safely keep them, they have not really gone.
We can see them in that second between awake and sleep,
And in the daytime shadows, our counsel they will keep.

Wonder

Kicking through the leaves and mud,
cloud and rain, easterly winds.
The day gloomed ahead of her. Her little girl,
ran and grinned, 'I'm a kite Mummy!'
Her arms spread as wide as her smile, wind-blown.

Puddles of earthy water littered the lane, clouds reflected.
More rain she thought, 'just great!'.
Red wellies jumped and splashed. 'Such fun Mummy!'
She twirled and danced in the water, laughing.

Bare branches creaked and groaned, bending to the force
that moved them. The lazy wind blew through her.
'The trees are dancing, see them?' 'I can dance too!'
She hopped and skipped her giggles lift the grey.

The rain eases, the wind drops, a watery sun shows through
clouds. 'Look, the sky has stopped crying!' The little girl
stoops down. Star fish hands open. 'Look Mummy,
the sun has made the flowers smile'

She looks down amongst the washed out debris, a Snowdrop.
She smiles. She looks down at her daughter.
Her eyes brightly shine. To be a child.
To see the world, so clearly and with such wonder.

Winter

The winters of my youth were very different from today,
Each year it seems to shift and change in many varied ways.
The long, hard frosts are very seldom to be seen,
And the trees hang on much longer to their canopies of green.
The flora and the fauna, just don't know what to do,
And clothing choice is tricky for the likes of me and you.

But winter is still winter although it's not as bleak,
And the shorter, darker, colder days, push us to go and seek,
Hearty stews, and apple pies, hot chocolate does the trick.
Sitting by an open fire watching the flames, spit and lick.
But remember all our little friends outside and in the cold.
And keep them fed and watered, to warm the chilly souls.

Badger *(meles meles)*

We are fascinating creatures, we roam around at night,
The largest british predator, we have very poor eyesight.
We have brilliant sense of hearing and amazing sense of smell.
Many years we have been here, oh the stories we could tell.

Almost hunted from existence, in the not-too-distant past,
Our clansmen shot and poisoned, hundreds more were trapped
and gassed. Our fur was prized for brushes, for vanity and paint,
Our setts were burned and buried, violence was not restrained.

These deeds dispersed the generations of badgers from their setts.
The perpetrators merely doing what they thought was for the best.
But in due course it so happened that badgers were so few,
Men passed an act of parliament to protect them, this was new!

So, we thrived and had our children, our cubs did very well,
Our setts grew large and in them, all of us could safely dwell,
Beneath the leafy woodlands and forests we lived free,
Until it was alleged that we make cows sick with TB!

The issue was debated, discussed and voted on,
How it was transmitted, and what it was that should be done,
And so, it was decided the badger was at fault,
Men put their heads together to plan a full assault.

And back we are at the beginning, hunted, trapped and killed,
This cull is slightly different, the men are much more skilled,
They bait us with snacks so tasty, that we cannot resist,
To dig them up and eat them, put ourselves at such high risk.

Our clans are divided, run in fear across the fields,
The past come back to haunt us, our cubs we cannot shield,
From all those who hate us, who just want us gone,
I hope they realise, just what it is they have done.

Can You See Me!

I was born in a body that does not conform,
To the way that society thinks is the norm.
Because I am different, I am either ignored,
Or stared at, made fun of or told I am flawed.
The things people miss when they see me like this,
Are the gifts I was born with, these gifts you dismiss.
I can name every bird in the sky as it sings,
I can see what they are, by the shape of their wings.
I can give you each verse of Shakespearean play,
I can repeat word for word all the things that you say,
Even spellings and science and stories I've heard,
I can tell you of them, yes, I can every word.
But as well as these things, there are two special gifts,
My heart is not complex, my love it uplifts.
My love for all creatures, be it big or be it small,
Is reflected to me, twice as much from them all.
So, when you see me, don't judge, don't pass by.
I am happy, I am blessed, I have gifts, don't be shy.

For Janice
With love

30

If - For the people of Ukraine

If I could launch one thousand ships to save you from this war,
I would this very moment, be sailing quickly to your shores.
I would take you many oceans from the chaos of your land,
And harbour you in safety until all weapons have been banned.

If I could ease the pain for all the loved ones you have lost,
I would help to share the burden, I would help to share the cost,
Of all the grief and heartache, of the memories left behind.
To comfort and restore you, to give you peace of mind.

If I could cry one thousand tears to put out all the fires,
That burn your homes and heartland, a roaring funeral pyre.
I would weep within an instant, and cleanse the burning soil,
And cool the once clear waters of rivers that now boil.

If I could be much more than just one person feeling sad,
If I could show the world that starting wars is just so bad,
If I could launch a thousand ships and save you all from harm.
I would save you all this minute, gathered safely in my arms.

Hill Pony Heroes

Four million years have seen me roam,
On ancient moorland, I call my home.
My hooves are small, my footsteps light,
But we are full of strength and might.

This strength was sought, to carry you,
Up to the mines, to haul and hew,
Rich minerals in the mines so stark,
Underground, damp, cold and dark.

We have hauled your rocks and stones,
Cold, tired and weary to our bones.
We have tilled your crops for you,
Not asked for much, a snack or two?

Our grazing keeps the moor alive,
We help the flora, grow, and thrive.
Because we treat the moor with care,
It's full of plants and lichens, rare.

We also have a special gene,
Unique to us and never seen,
In other equines, so you see,
You need us here, so let us be!

For generations, past and now,
The commoners were made a vow,
For grazing rights, and rights to roam,
Across the land around their homes.

Along with us, the Dartmoor Hillies,
Non country folk, within the cities,
Not looking at the bigger picture,
Changing laws and getting stricter.

Commoners without their land,
Shooting ponies where they stand.
Stealing ground without remorse,
Not thinking of the little horse,
Who quietly, guards and tends the moor,
Without them there's no moor for sure.

Photo supplied by Melanie Barrett

Wez

I know you sit beside me and cry before I'm gone,
I know that your decision has been the hardest one.
I thank you for inviting me to be your best loyal friend,
I know that you have loved me until the very end.

Sometimes the hardest loving thing,
the hardest thing to do,
Is the very kindest and the
best that you can do.
I love you for the tears you cry,
I love you for your smile,
I am sorry that my leaving you,
makes you want to cry.

I have had the best in life,
I know that this is true,
And even if not here today,
my love remains with you.
A bit of you comes with me when I have to go.
But a bit of me is left behind, just to let you know.

I'm not here to comfort you, while sad and crying tears,
In time you will reflect on so many happy years.
I am here beside you, no matter what you do.
Although you cannot see me, my heart's still loving you.

For Sue and Mike
with love, Judy 27.05.21

Just One More Day

Just one more day is all I ask for, to spend more time with you.
You have been beside me every day since life was new.
You held me in your love, you spoke with words so wise,
How will I be me without you, there to be my guide?
Just one more day.

Just one more day is all I ask for, to have my hand in yours.
To see the rough and hard worked skin, from all the daily chores.
You worked so hard to keep me, safe and free from harm.
How I long to be encircled, within those loving arms.
Just one more day.

Just one more day is all I ask for, to sit and talk with you.
I often didn't listen to all the things you knew.
Now I would sit in silence, hang on every word you say.
But it's too late to do that, now you have gone away.
Just one more day.

Just one more day is all I ask for, to tell you I love you.
My love it could not hold you, even though my love was true.
Every hour, every minute it hurts so much to breathe.
I wish that it was me, not you, that had to go and leave.
Just one more day.

Just one more day is all I ask for, learn to smile through the rain.
Some time to try and mend, some time to ease the pain.
Of losing one so dear to me, leaving such an empty space.
Perhaps I'll learn to live with just the memory of your face.
Just one more day.

Tinsell's Story -

She was feeling so cold, and so very hungry. She knew that she didn't have many months in her and had managed to survive life, produce and nurture her babies. She had never felt so ill, as she searched around the bins in the car park for a few scraps and knew her hours were quite literally her last. A few passers-by had seen her and some had screamed as they mistook her identity for something else. Some just ignored her and some pointed and laughed. She was just about to give up when she heard someone coming near, she tried to hide but just didn't have the strength left to move. Friend or foe she would just have to accept whatever was to be. However, to her surprise, she heard a gentle voice tell her that she was going to be helped, not to be scared and not to give up, all would be well.

A long journey later, I met up with another gentle voice person who helped me warm up, helped me with a warm drink and a little food, I couldn't take too much as I had been starving for so long and my face was so painful. I had been in pain for some considerable time. I was bathed, my sores were cleaned and I was given something that made me feel a bit whoozy but took away the discomfort. The last thing I remember that day was being wrapped in something so very soft and a voice telling me that 'all would be well'. Many days passed in that warm place. They helped me eat and drink, they gave me medication to soothe the pain and take away the infection. My swollen face started to return to normal and I felt weak but stronger and more comfortable than I done for a very long time.

A discussion was had about whether I was strong enough to have an operation to remove the pain once and for all. My new friends decided that it would be the best thing in the long run to go ahead and then I would recover more quickly.
I was taken to a hospital and I was carefully looked after and I remember going to sleep, the last words I heard were 'All will be well'

I woke up back in my warm, safe place and once again I wanted for nothing. Every need was taken care of and eventually I was able to help myself to a bit of soft food and water. Eventually, after many weeks had passed, I grew strong, I gained the weight I had lost, I looked more recognisable and made a lot of friends. I know I was special as I always had extra special treatment and a choice of what to eat. I was always told how special I was and how much they loved me.

Summer came and I was well enough to take a few strolls outside. It was so good to hear the bird song, smell the herbs and flowers and feel alive again. Soon I was able to live in my own home within the grounds of the place I now called home and was living quite a nice semi-retirement.

September came in with a bit of a nip in the air, I had gained some noisy neighbours who didn't really get on with each other and I didn't feel quite right again. This time a man found me, in my home and I didn't feel very well at all. He took me to the lady I always felt safe with and I could tell she was very concerned about me.

'All will be well'

I was held and comforted, I was wrapped in something very soft and given something to make me feel better, I was told that I was loved and I was special and that 'all will be well'.

I felt a bit better that night and ate a good meal but the next day I felt poorly again and I had a strange taste in my mouth. I was held, bathed, given something to help me feel comfortable and put to bed on a warm, soft mattress. I had a visitor who had got to know me well during my stay and she spent quite a bit of time with me and I thought, 'All will be well'.

The next day I couldn't raise my head off my pillow, I didn't feel any pain but I couldn't eat or drink. I heard the lady talk about giving me some fluid therapy but as I was so peaceful she didn't want to cause me any distress, I didn't really understand but I enjoyed her company for a while and went to sleep until she came back. I heard her tell me how special I was and what a difference I had made to my kind, as there aren't many of us left now. I was too tired to think much and I was warm and cosy, it was so nice to be loved and cared for and to have a name, I didn't know about those, to my kind, we just are, we have no names.

A little while later I awoke, I felt so light and young and free, how amazing, the lady came in to see me, she put her hand on my back and said, 'Oh Tinsell, you have left us, we have loved you so much and you have drawn so many people into understanding the plight of your kind, you will never be forgotten' Then tears fell.

My body is buried in the garden, in a place where the lady walks by very often. My spirit lives on in the hearts of the people who are trying to save us. As long as there are people like all of you, 'All will be well'.

My thanks to you all for giving me a second chance and a last peaceful and dignified few months.

My name is Tinsell and I was loved.

RIP Tinsell 10/09/2020 xx

About the Author

Although I was born in London, I have lived in Devon since 1963, a good year to arrive here as it was one of the worst winters on record! Most of this time I have remained in the village of Stoke Fleming, or very near-by. We are in an Area of Outstanding Natural Beauty and very fortunate to be a pebble's throw away from one of South Devon's most beautiful beaches, Blackpool Sands.

As a toddler I was fascinated by the outdoors and all the creatures I found in it, although I am still not a fan of spiders, they need to be admired from afar! At the age of 31, I took an injured tawny owl to my mum who simply said, 'I would have thought that you would have grown out of this by now!' Well, I am now 62 and I have shown no signs of this yet!

Both my parents were ahead of their time and brought myself and my five siblings up in an almost self-sufficient life, in tune with and respectful of nature.

15 years ago, Alan and I were newly together, and I disturbed a nest of hedgehogs in one of our stables, purely accidentally. I carefully tucked them all back up where I had found them and left them be. Sadly, on return later that day all babies were scattered around the stable, one was missing, one was dead and the remaining two were peeping away in distress. I duly gathered them up, tucked them down my shirt for warmth and brought them home.

All we had was an ear dropper, some goats milk, a hot water bottle and a cardboard box. Against all the odds we successfully raised 'Piglet' and 'Roo' to adulthood. I remember saying to Alan, (while sitting up in bed, cross eyed with tiredness, trying to 'toilet' a hoglet) "it's only going to get worse, you had better quit now" Having now had many years gaining knowledge and experience with the help of other rescues, research, and our wonderful vets, I would not recommend this to anyone inexperienced.

En-route with Alan to the Coronation Concert May 2023

Alan, my partner, is a true countryman and from a farming family. He is a fount of all knowledge and can identify most birdsong straight away, which is something I am most envious of!

A few creatures of various sorts found their way to us, as people became aware of our willingness to help - word soon gets around! We moved house 10 years ago and for the first year we had no wild patients at all. And then, suddenly, it was as if there was an invisible sign on the door! We had had the footings dug for a conservatory/boot room and the next day there were two hedgehogs in the bottom of it. Alan was heard to say, "they have found us, now there will be no end to it!" Well, we soon found ourselves looking after 40 hedgehogs of various sizes and descriptions and I was beginning to struggle with work, hedgehogs and family.

Fast forward to the Covid pandemic and we decided to register Prickles in a Pickle as a charity. This basically was a vehicle to raising money and accessing grants, as we had been funding this ourselves and it was getting a bit expensive.

Judy with the Coronation Champion Certificate and Medal

We now have 34 volunteers, six trustees and up to 170 hedgehogs in residence at any given time and take in between 900 and 1400 every year. We have students working towards their Duke of Edinburgh scheme medals through us and veterinary students in placement too. We also have volunteers who come through the social prescribing scheme, from time to time. We still run from home at the moment, although we are fundraising to purchase land, to move the hospital to a purpose-built building. Alan and I work as a team, and we can't do this without each other. Our volunteers are invaluable to us and come from all walks of life.

In the last 18 months our endeavours seem to have been recognised as I was nominated for the 2022 BBC Radio Devon 'Make a Difference Award' and was delighted to be given a Highly Commended Award in the Environmental Category. And the icing on the cake came when I received a Coronation Champion Award - one of only 500 awards given out by their majesties, King Charles III and Queen Camilla through the Royal Voluntary Service, celebrating extraordinary volunteers across the country who have been contributing to their communities. The award included an invitation for myself and Alan to see the Coronation Concert at Windsor Castle - an incredible experience that we will never forget!

In fact 2023 has been a year to remember - as we were also visited by Gillian Burke and the BBC One Show who filmed a piece highlighting the plight of hedgehogs coming out of hibernation too early because of climate change. It was such an honour for our rescue centre to be chosen for this and gave the charity prime time coverage to millions of viewers.

I started writing again during the pandemic and have been asked many times to put my scribblings in print which I now have, with the help of one of our volunteers who just happens to be in the business.

Any proceeds from the sale of this book will be split equally between myself and the hedgehogs that we help and who I love so dearly.